SCAN THE CODE TO ACCESS YOUR FREE DIGITAL COPY

SCAN ME

THIS BOOK BELONGS TO

TO

_____

TABLE OF CONTENTS

LOBES AND LOBULES OF THE BRAIN (LATERAL AND SUPERIOR VIEW)

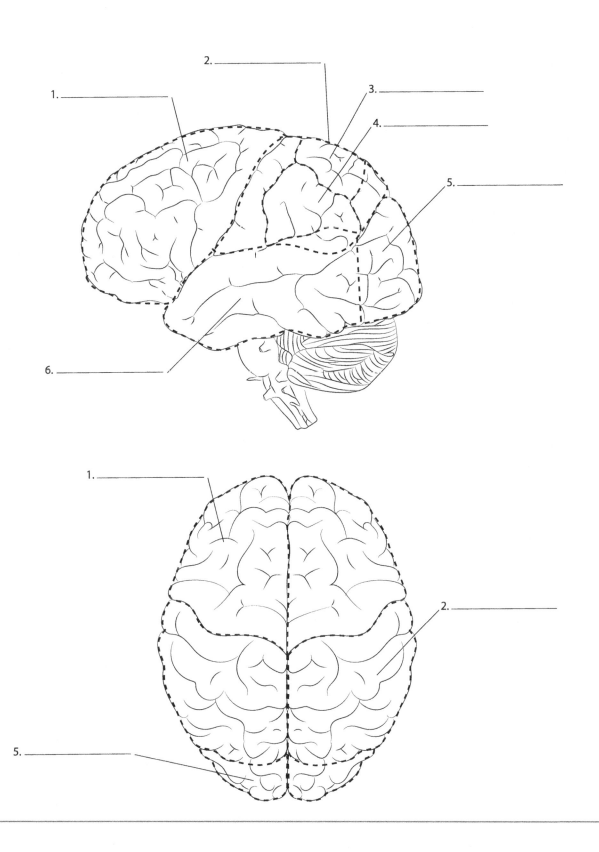

LOBES AND LOBULES OF THE BRAIN (LATERAL VIEW)

1. Frontal lobe

2. Parietal lobe

3. Superior parietal lobule

4. Inferior parietal lobule

5. Occipital lobe

6. Temporal lobe

GYRI AND SULCI OF THE HUMAN BRAIN (LATERAL VIEW)

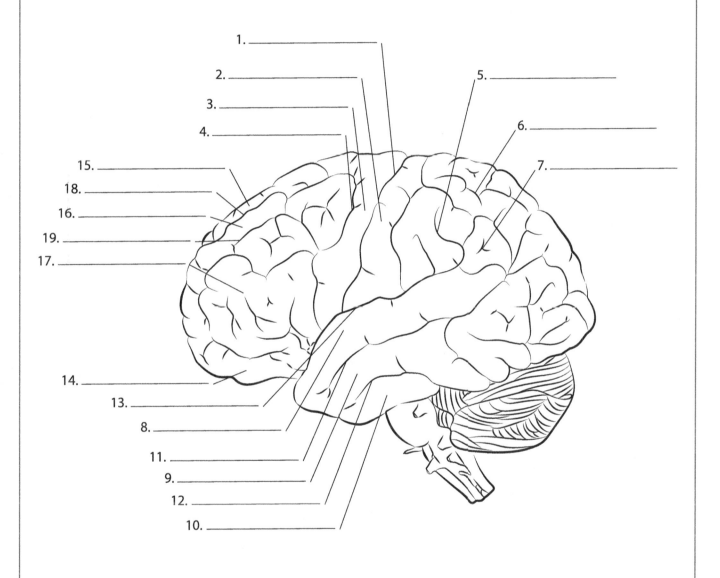

1. _____
2. _____
3. _____
4. _____
5. _____
6. _____
7. _____
15. _____
18. _____
16. _____
19. _____
17. _____
14. _____
13. _____
8. _____
11. _____
9. _____
12. _____
10. _____

GYRI AND SULCI OF THE HUMAN BRAIN (LATERAL VIEW)

1. Central sulcus (Rolando)
2. Postcentral gyrus
3. Precentral gyrus
4. Precentral sulcus
5. Supramarginal gyrus
6. Intraparietal sulcus
7. Angular gyrus
8. Superior temporal gyrus
9. Middle temporal gyrus
10. Inferior temporal gyrus
11. Superior temporal sulcus
12. Middle temporal sulcus
13. Lateral (Sylvian) sulcus
14. Orbital gyrus
15. Superior frontal gyrus
16. Middle frontal gyrus
17. Inferior frontal gyrus
18. Superior frontal sulcus
19. Inferior frontal sulcus

INFERIOR VIEW OF THE HUMAN BRAIN

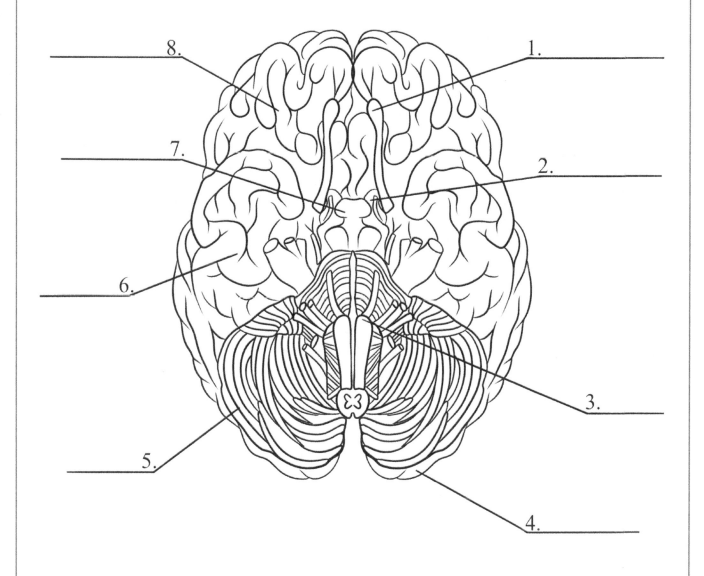

INFERIOR VIEW OF THE HUMAN BRAIN

1. Olfactory bulb

2. Optic chiasm

3. Brain stem

4. Occipital lobe

5. Cerebellum

6. Temporal lobe

7. Infundibulum

8. Frontal lobe

FUNCTIONAL AREAS OF THE HUMAN BRAIN (LATERAL VIEW)

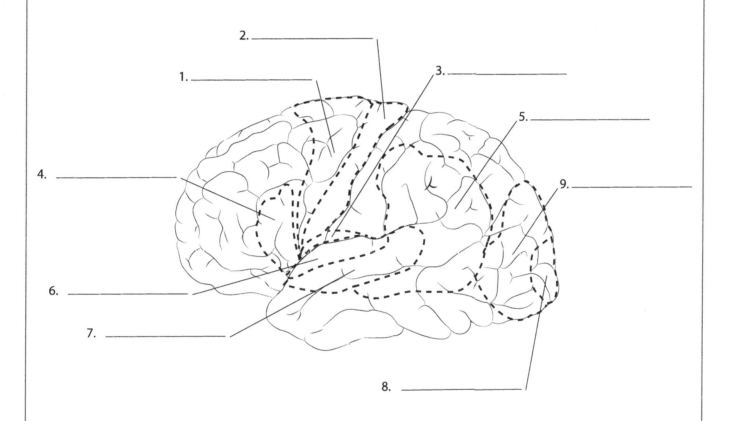

FUNCTIONAL AREAS OF THE HUMAN BRAIN (LATERAL VIEW)

1. Primary motor area

2. Primary sensory area

3. Secondary motor and sensory area

4. Anterior (motor) speech area (Broca's area)

5. Posterior (sensory) speech area (Wernicke's area)

6. Primary auditory area

7. Secondary auditory area

8. Primary visual area

9. Secondary visual area

SAGITTAL SECTION OF THE HUMAN BRAIN

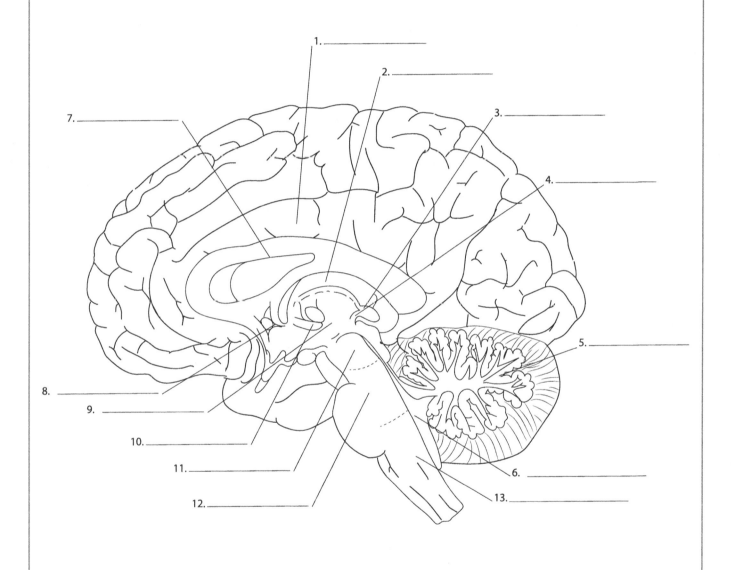

SAGITTAL SECTION OF THE HUMAN BRAIN

1. Cingulate gyrus
2. Fornix
3. Pineal gland
4. Posterior commissure
5. Cerebellum
6. Forth ventricle
7. Corpus callosum
8. Anterior commissure
9. Diencephalon
10. Hypothalamic sulcus
11. Midbrain
12. Pons
13. Medulla oblongata

CORONAL SECTION OF THE HUMAN BRAIN

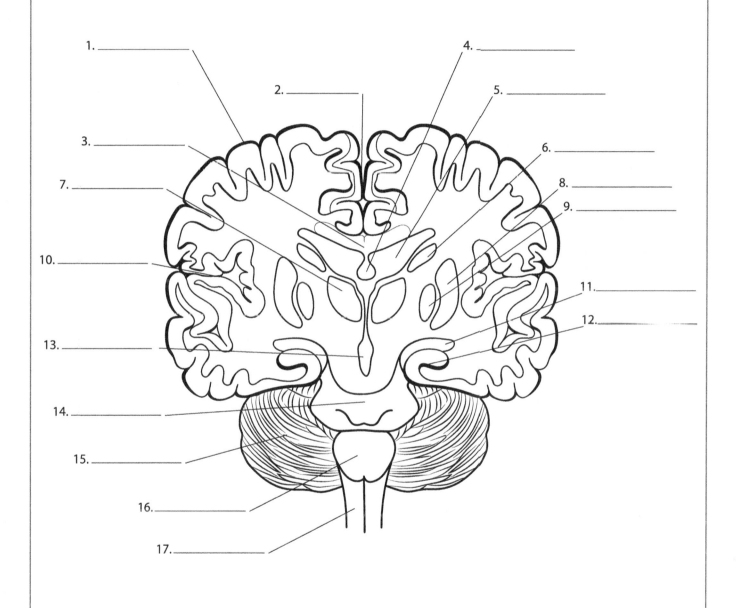

1. _____

2. _____

3. _____

4. _____

5. _____

6. _____

7. _____

8. _____

9. _____

10. _____

11. _____

12. _____

13. _____

14. _____

15. _____

16. _____

17. _____

CORONAL SECTION OF THE HUMAN BRAIN

1. Cerebral cortex
2. Longitudinal fissure
3. Corpus callosum
4. Fornix
5. Lateral ventricle
6. Caudate nucleus
7. Thalamus
8. Putamen
9. Globus pallidus
10. Lateral sulcus
11. Hippocampus
12. Hippocampal gyrus
13. Third ventricle
14. Pons
15. Cerebellum
16. Medulla oblongata
17. Spinal cord

CRANIAL NERVES

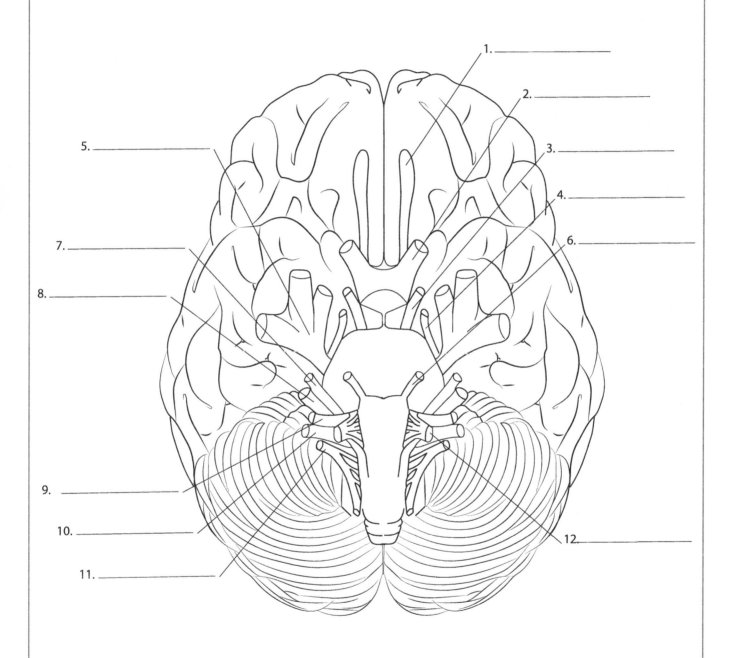

CRANIAL NERVES

1. Olfactory
2. Optic
3. Oculomotor
4. Trochlear
5. Trigeminal
6. Abducens
7. Facial
8. Vestibulocochlear
9. Glossopharyngeal
10. Vagus
11. Accessory
12. Hypoglossal

TRANSVERSE SECTION OF THE MIDBRAIN

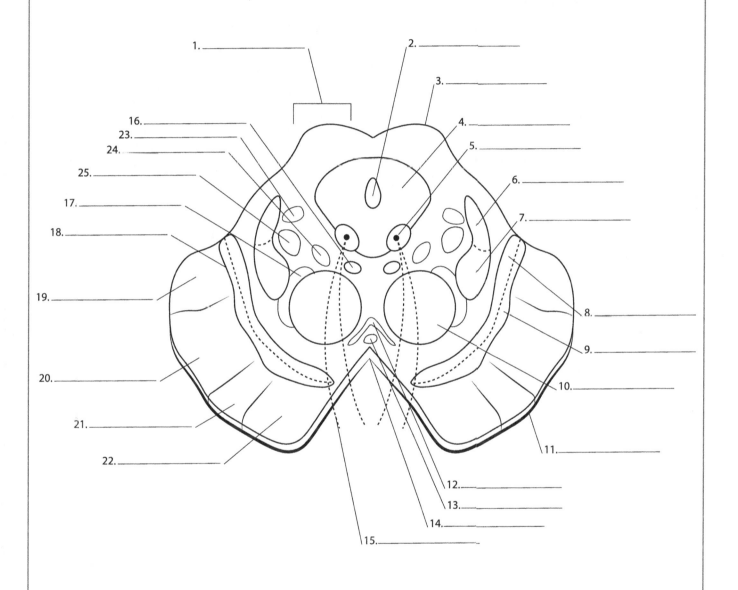

1. _____
2. _____
3. _____
4. _____
5. _____
6. _____
7. _____
8. _____
9. _____
10. _____
11. _____
12. _____
13. _____
14. _____
15. _____
16. _____
17. _____
18. _____
19. _____
20. _____
21. _____
22. _____
23. _____
24. _____
25. _____

TRANSVERSE SECTION OF THE MIDBRAIN

1. Tectum
2. Cerebral aqueduct
3. Superior colliculus
4. Periaqueductal grey (PAG)
5. Oculomotor nucleus
6. Spinothalamic and trigeminothalamic tracts
7. Medial lemniscus
8. Pars compacta
9. Pars reticulata
10. Red nucleus
11. Crus cerebri
12. Anterior tegmental decussation
13. Interpeduncular nucleus
14. Ventral tegmental area
15. Root fibres of oculomotor nerve
16. Medial longitudinal fasciculus
17. Cerebellothalamic fibres
18. Substantia nigra
19. Parieto-, occipito-, temporopontine fibres
20. Corticospinal fibres
21. Corticonuclear (corticobulbar) fibres
22. Frontopontine fibres
23. Posterior trigeminothalamic fibres
24. Central tegmental tract
25. Anterior trigeminothalamic fibres

TRANSVERSE SECTION OF THE PONS (UPPER PART AND LOWER PART)

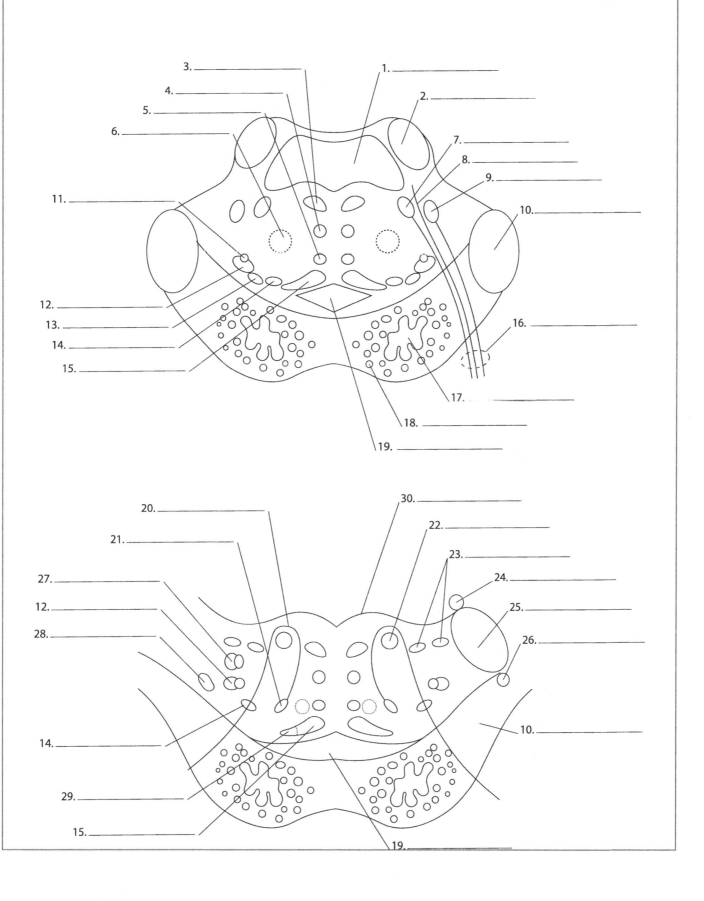

TRANSVERSE SECTION OF THE PONS (UPPER PART AND LOWER PART)

1. Fourth ventricle
2. Superior cerebellar peduncle
3. Medial longitudinal bundle
4. Tectospinal tract
5. Rubrospinal tract
6. Central tegmental tract
7. Motor nucleus of trigeminal nerve
8. Mesencephalic root of trigeminal nerve
9. Main sensory nucleus of trigeminal nerve
10. Middle cerebellar peduncle
11. Superior olivary nucleus
12. Lateral lemniscus
13. Spinal lemniscus
14. Trigeminal lemniscus
15. Medial lemniscus
16. Trigeminal nerve
17. Corticospinal and corticonuclear fibres
18. Pontine nuclei
19. Trapezoid body
20. Facial nerve
21. Nucleus of facial nerve
22. Abducent nucleus
23. Vestibular nuclei
24. Dorsal cochlear nucleus
25. Inferior cerebellar peduncle
26. Ventral cochlear nucleus
27. Spinal nucleus and tract of trigeminal nerve
28. Ventral spinocerebellar tract
29. Anterior spinothalamic tract
30. Facial colliculus

TRANSVERSE SECTION OF THE MEDULLA
(AT THE LEVEL OF OLIVE)

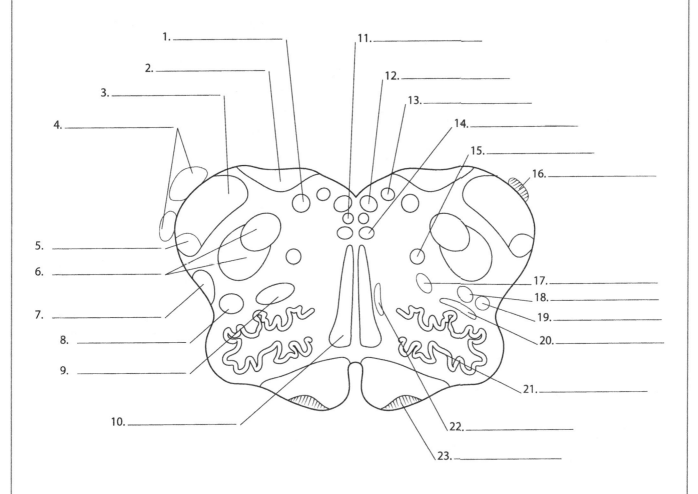

1. _____
2. _____
3. _____
4. _____
5. _____
6. _____
7. _____
8. _____
9. _____
10. _____
11. _____
12. _____
13. _____
14. _____
15. _____
16. _____
17. _____
18. _____
19. _____
20. _____
21. _____
22. _____
23. _____

TRANSVERSE SECTION OF THE MEDULLA (AT THE LEVEL OF OLIVE)

1. Solitary tract nucleus
2. Vestibular nuclei
3. Inferior cerebral peduncle
4. Cochlear nuclei
5. Dorsal spinocerebellar tract
6. Spinal nucleus and tract of the trigeminal nerve
7. Ventral spinocerebellar tract
8. Lateral spinothalamic and spinotectal tracts
9. Anterior spinothalamic tract
10. Medial lemniscus
11. Medial longitudinal fasiculus
12. Hypoglossal nucleus
13. Dorsal vagal nucleus
14. Tectospinal tract
15. Nucleus ambiguus
16. Pontobulbar body
17. Vestibulospinal tract
18. Lateral reticular nucleus
19. Rubrospinal tract
20. Dorsal accessory olivary nucleus
21. Inferior olivary nucleus
22. Medial accessory olivary nucleus
23. Arcuate nucleus

THE CIRCLE OF WILLIS

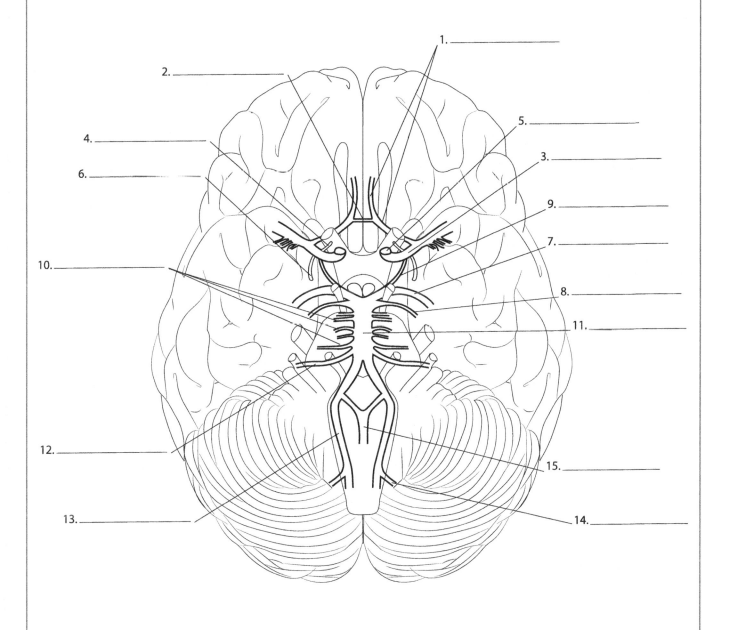

1. _____

2. _____

4. _____

6. _____

5. _____

3. _____

9. _____

7. _____

10. _____

8. _____

11. _____

12. _____

15. _____

13. _____

14. _____

THE CIRCLE OF WILLIS

1. Anterior cerebral artery
2. Anterior communicating artery
3. Middle cerebral artery
4. Ophtalmic artery
5. Internal carotid artery
6. Anterior choroidal artery
7. Posterior cerebral artery
8. Superior cerebellar artery
9. Posterior communicating artery
10. Pontine arteries
11. Basilar artery
12. Anterior inferior cerebellar artery
13. Vertebral artery
14. Posterior inferior cerebellar artery
15. Anterior spinal artery

LIMBIC SYSTEM
(BASAL GANGLIA REMOVED)

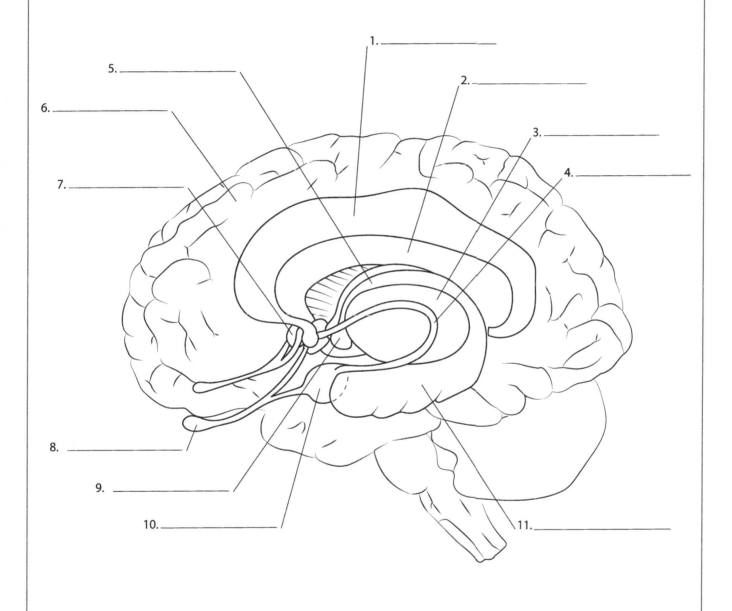

LIMBIC SYSTEM
(BASAL GANGLIA REMOVED)

1. Cingulate cortex
2. Corpus callosum
3. Thalamus
4. Stria terminalis
5. Fornix
6. Frontal cortex
7. Septum
8. Olfactory bulb
9. Mammillary body
10. Amygdala
11. Hippocampus

CORONAL VIEW (1)

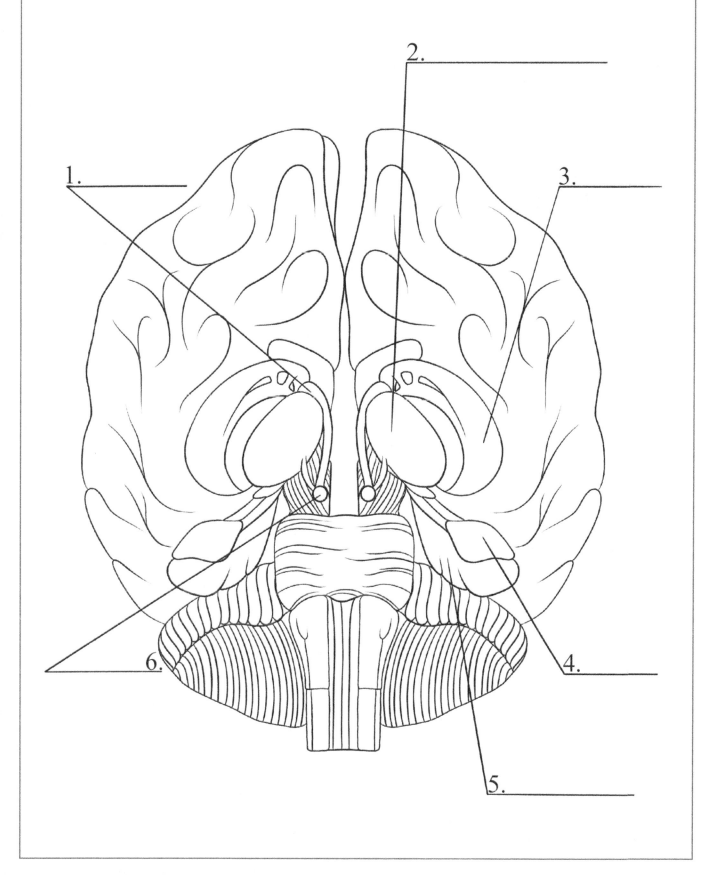

1.

2.

3.

4.

5.

6.

CORONAL VIEW (1)

1. Fornix
2. Thalamus
3. Putamen
4. Amygdala
5. Hippocampus
6. Mammillary body

CORONAL VIEW (2)

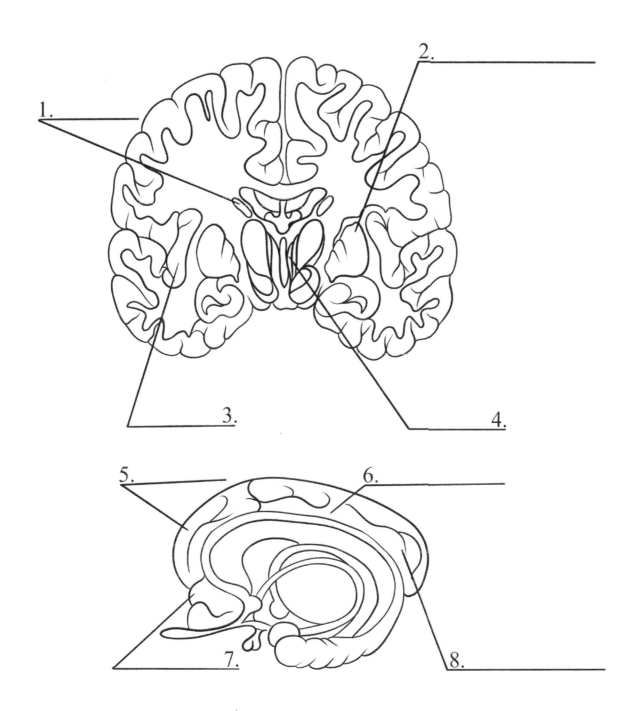

1.

2.

3.

4.

5.

6.

7.

8.

CORONAL VIEW (2)

1. Caudate nucleus

2. Putamen

3. Insula

4. Nucleus accumbens

5. Anterior cingulate cortex

6. Mid cingulate cortex

7. Subgenual anterior

8. Posterior cingulate cortex

PROTECTIVE STRUCTURES
OF THE BRAIN

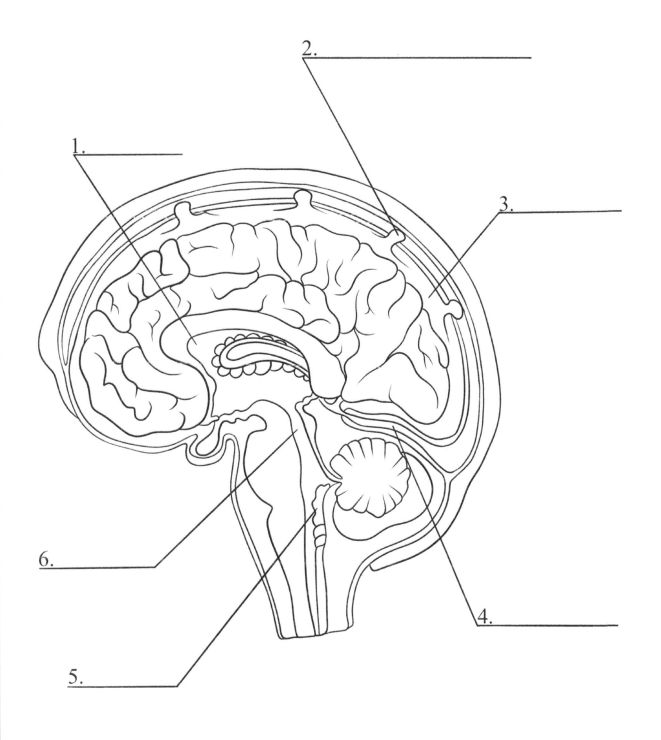

PROTECTIVE STRUCTURES OF THE BRAIN

1. Third ventricle
2. Arachnoid villus
3. Subarachnoid space
4. Straight sinus
5. Choroid plexus
6. Cerebral aqueduct

MIDSAGITTAL VIEW

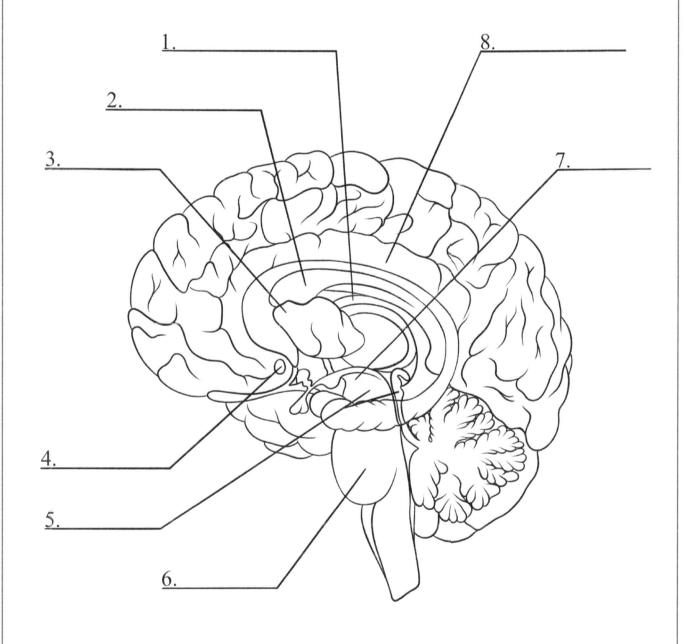

1.

2.

3.

4.

5.

6.

7.

8.

MIDSAGITTAL VIEW

1. Fornix

2. Caudate

3. Putamen

4. Nucleus accumbens

5. Midbrain

6. Pons

7. Ventra tegmentum

8. Cingulate cortex

CRANIAL NERVES BOTTOM VIEW

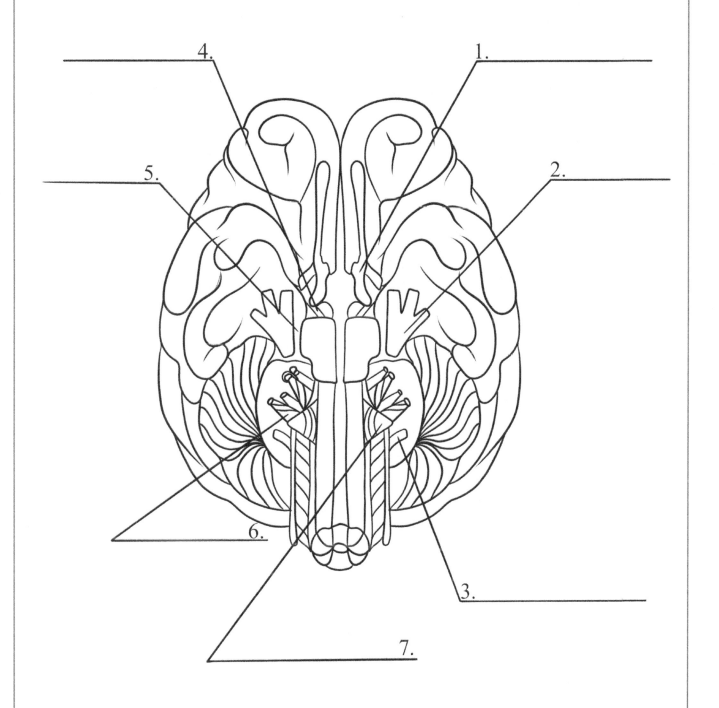

4.

1.

5.

2.

6.

3.

7.

CRANIAL NERVES BOTTOM VIEW

1. Optic nerve
2. Trigeminal nerve
3. Accessory nerve
4. Oculomotor nerve
5. Trochlear nerve
6. Vagus nerve
7. Hypoglossal nerve

THALAMUS

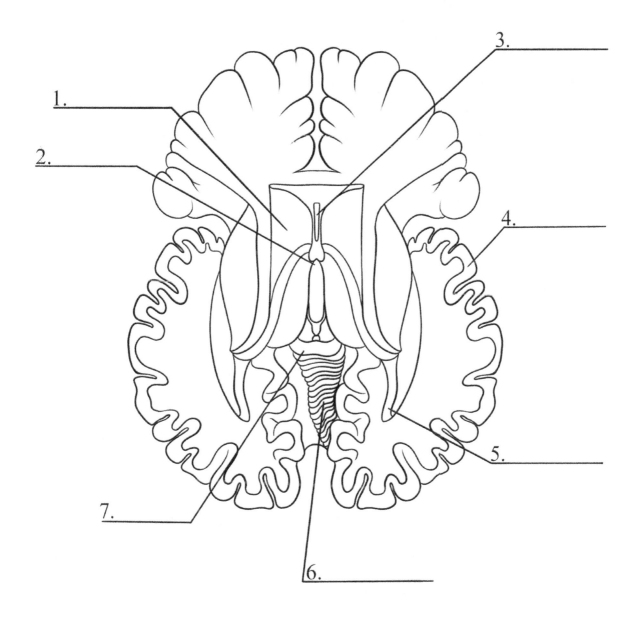

THALAMUS

1.   Head of caudate nucleus
2.   Anterior commissure
3.   Cavity of septum pellucidum
4.   Cortex of temporal lobe
5.   Posterior horn of lateral ventricle
6.   Vermis of cerebellum
7.   Inferior coillculus

BLOOD SUPPLY OF THE CENTRAL NERVOUS SYSTEM

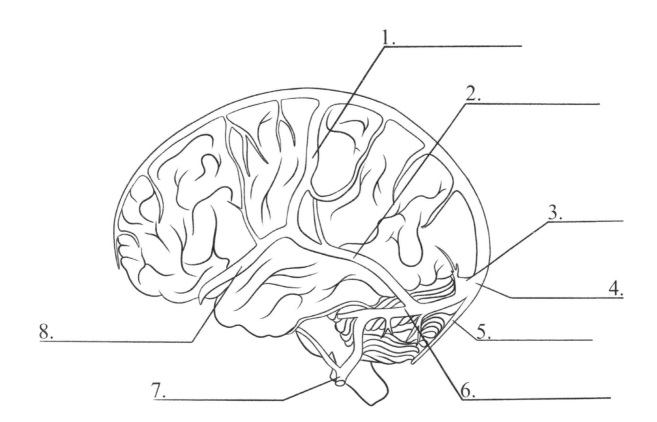

1.

2.

3.

4.

5.

6.

7.

8.

BLOOD SUPPLY OF THE CENTRAL NERVOUS SYSTEM

1.Superior anastomotic vein of Troland

2. Inferior anastomotic vein of Labbe

3. Straight sinus

4. Confluence of sinuses

5. Occipital sinus

6. Transverse sinus

7. Internal jugular vein

8. Superficial middle cerebral vein

BLOOD SUPPLY OF THE
CENTRAL NERVOUS SYSTEM

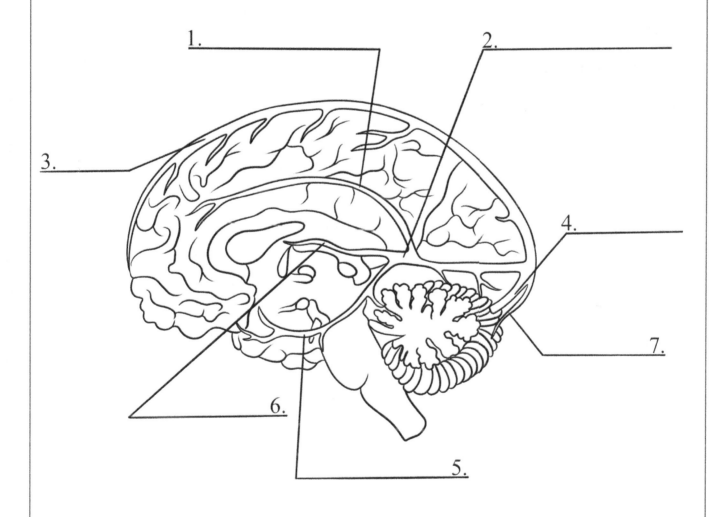

BLOOD SUPPLY OF THE CENTRAL NERVOUS SYSTEM

1. Inferior anastomotic
2. Great vein of Galen
3. Superior sagittal sinus
4. Transverse sinus
5. Basal vein of Rosenthal
6. Internal cerebral vein
7. Occipital sinus

BLOOD VESSEL DISTRIBUTION

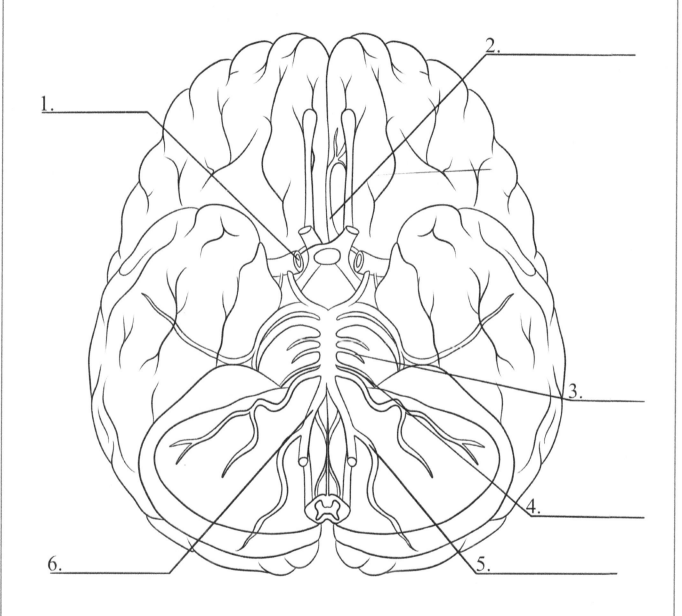

1.

2.

3.

4.

5.

6.

BLOOD VESSEL DISTRIBUTION

1. Internal carotid

2. Anterior cerebral

3. Pontine

4. Labyrinthine

5. Posterior inferior cerebellar

6. Vertebral

CEREBRAL HEMISPHERES

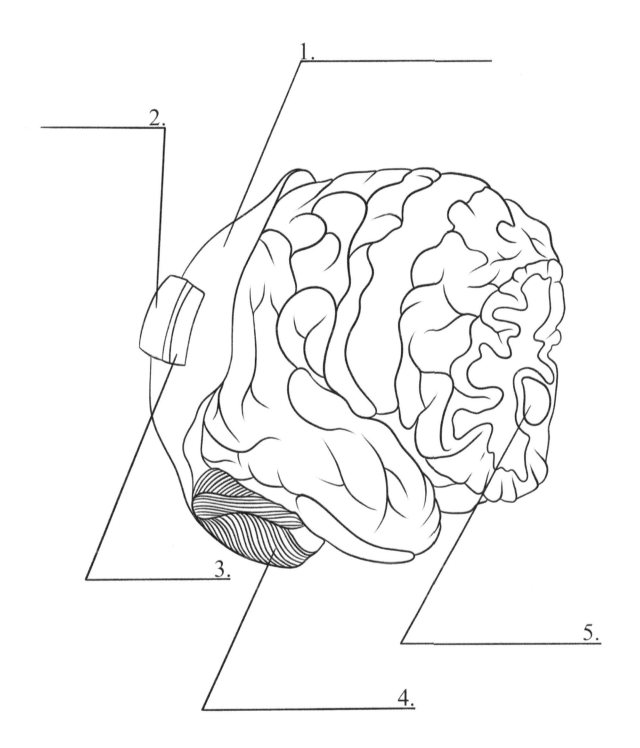

1. _____

2. _____

3. _____

4. _____

5. _____

CEREBRAL HEMISPHERES

1. Dura mater

2. Scalp

3. Skull

4. Cerebellum

5. Cerebrospinal fluid circulates within the ventricles

CIRCULATION OF CEREBROSPINAL FLUID

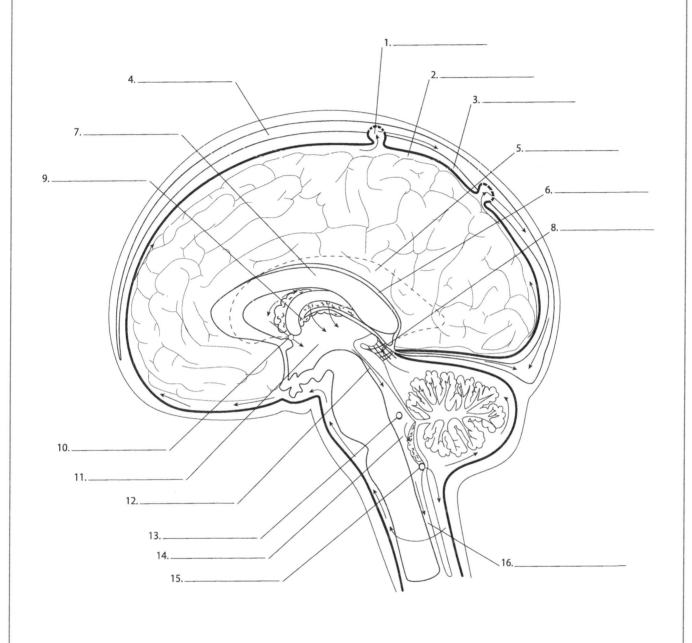

CIRCULATION OF CEREBROSPINAL FLUID

1. Arachnoid granulations
2. Subarachnoid space
3. Meningeal dura mater
4. Superior sagittal sinus
5. Lateral ventricle
6. Inferior sagittal sinus
7. Corpus callosum
8. Sinus cavernosus
9. Choroid plexus
10. Interventricular foramen of Monro
11. Third ventricle
12. Cerebral aqueduct (aqueduct of Sylvius)
13. Lateral foramen of Luschka
14. Fourth ventricle
15. Foramen of Magendie (median aperture)
16. Central canal

VENTRICLES OF THE BRAIN

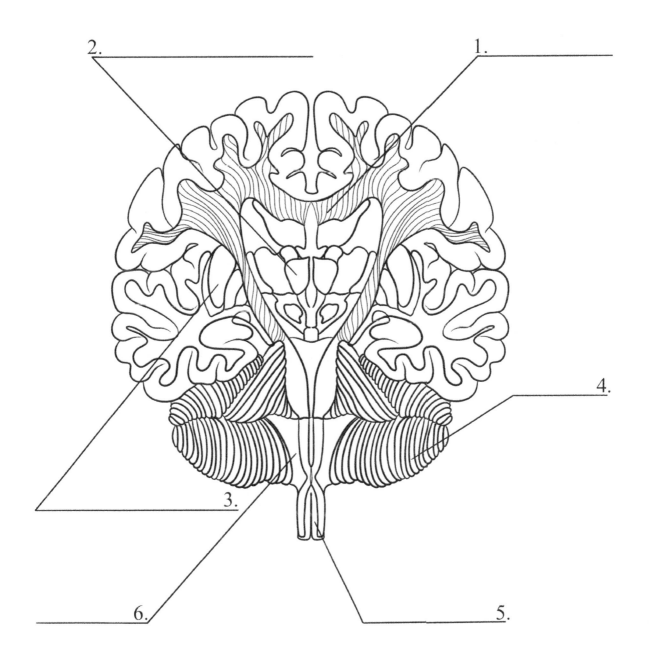

2. _____

1. _____

4. _____

3. _____

6. _____

5. _____

Ventricles of the Brain

1. Corpus
2. Thalamus
3. Putamen
4. Cerebellum
5. Spinal cord
6. Medulla

VISUAL SYSTEM

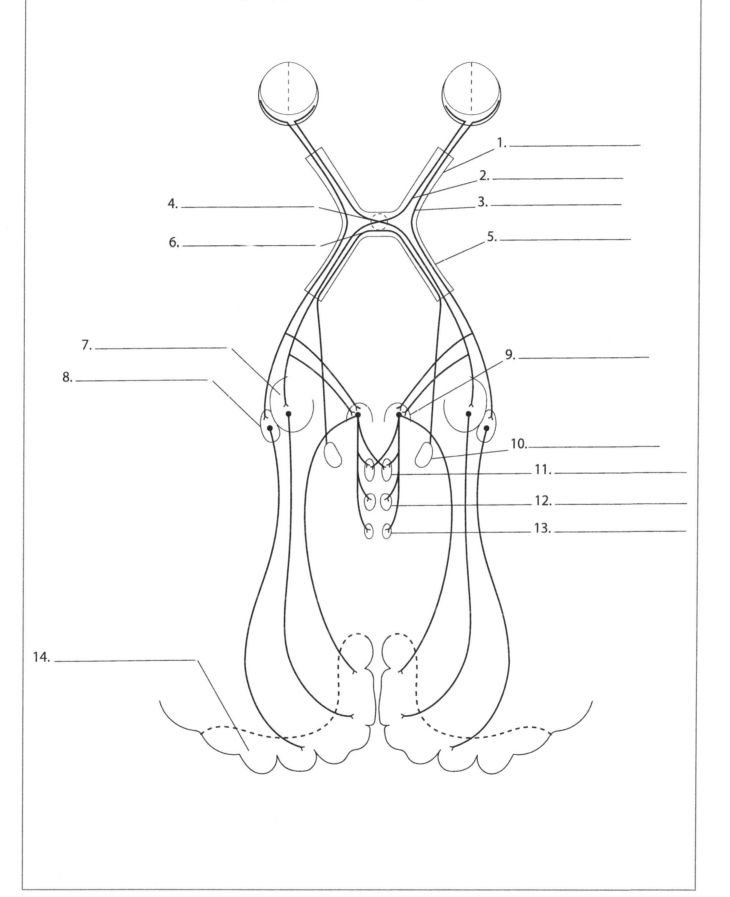

VISUAL SYSTEM

1. Optic nerve
2. Crossing fibres
3. Uncrossing fibres
4. Optic chiasma
5. Optic tract
6. Commissure of Guden
7. Pulvinar
8. Lateral geniculate body
9. Superior colliculus
10. Medial geniculate body
11. Nucleus of oculomotor nerve
12. Nucleus of trochlear nerve
13. Nucleus of abducent nerve
14. Cortex of occipital lobes

TRIGEMINAL NERVE

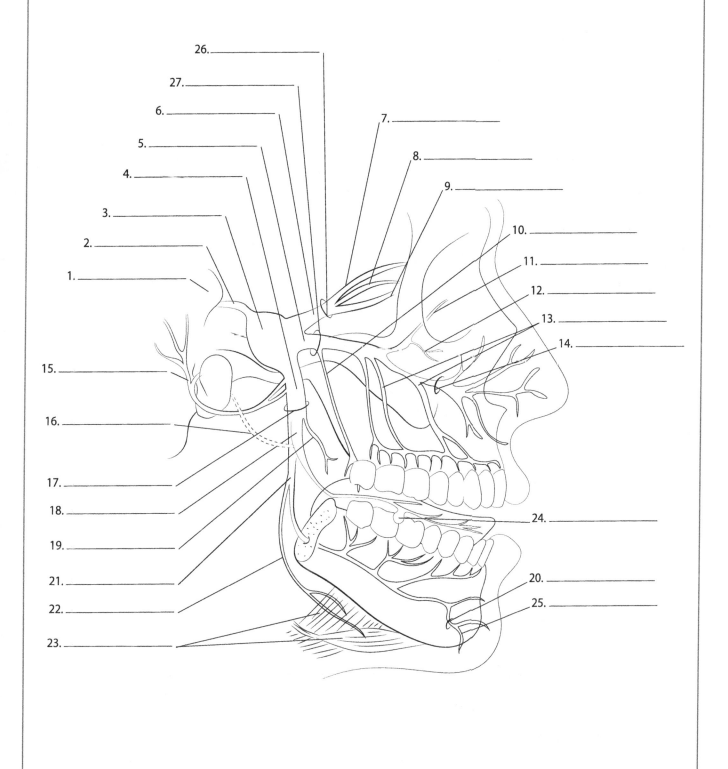

26. _____

27. _____

6. _____

5. _____

4. _____

3. _____

2. _____

1. _____

7. _____

8. _____

9. _____

10. _____

11. _____

12. _____

13. _____

14. _____

15. _____

16. _____

17. _____

18. _____

19. _____

21. _____

22. _____

23. _____

24. _____

20. _____

25. _____

TRIGEMINAL NERVE

1. Pons
2. Trigeminal nerve
3. Trigeminal ganglion (V)
4. Mandibular division (V3)
5. Maxillary division (V2)
6. Ophtalmic division (V1)
7. Facial nerve
8. Lacrimal nerve
9. Nasociliary nerve
10. Nervi palatini (majores and minores)
11. Infraorbital nerve
12. Zygomatic nerve
13. Superior alveolar nerves
14. Infraorbital foramen
15. Auriculotemporal nerve
16. Chorda tympani
17. Foramen ovale
18. Lingual nerve
19. Buccal nerve
20. Mental foramen
21. Inferior alveolar nerves
22. Mylohyoid nerve
23. Mylohyoid muscle, anterior belly of digastric muscle
24. Submandibular ganglion
25. Mental nerve
26. Superior orbital fissure
27. Foramen rotundum

BASIC NEURON TYPES

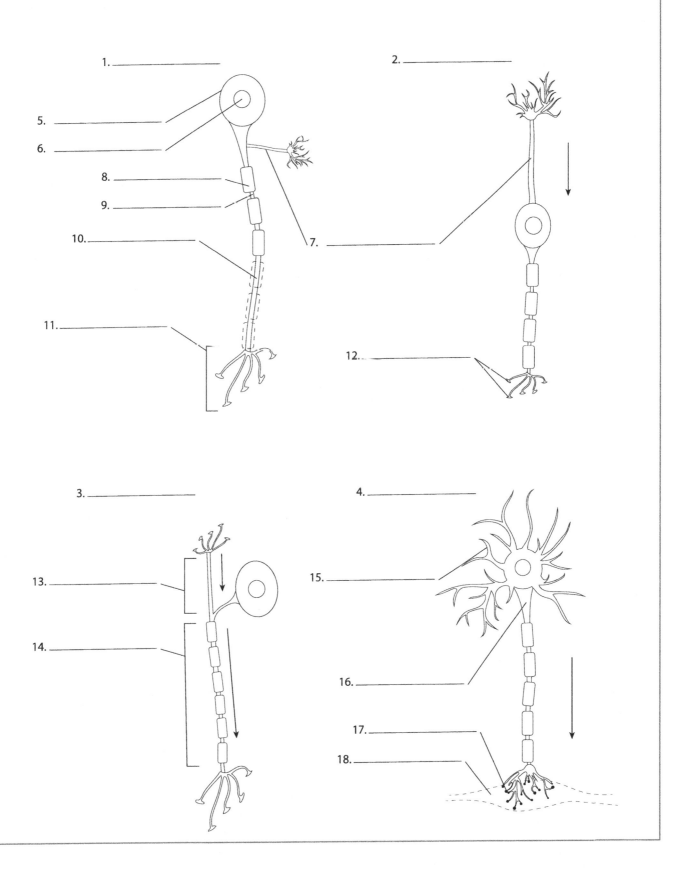

1. _____

2. _____

5. _____

6. _____

8. _____

9. _____

10. _____

7. _____

11. _____

12. _____

3. _____

4. _____

13. _____

15. _____

14. _____

16. _____

17. _____

18. _____

BASIC NEURON TYPES

1. Unipolar neuron
2. Bipolar neuron
3. Pseudounipolar neuron
4. Multipolar neuron
5. Cell body
6. Nucleus
7. Dendrite
8. Myelin sheath
9. Node of Ranvier
10. Axon
11. Telodendria (axon terminals)
12. Terminal buttons
13. Peripheral branch
14. Central branch
15. Dendrites
16. Axon hillock
17. Neuro-muscle synapses
18. Muscle

SPINAL CORD ANATOMY

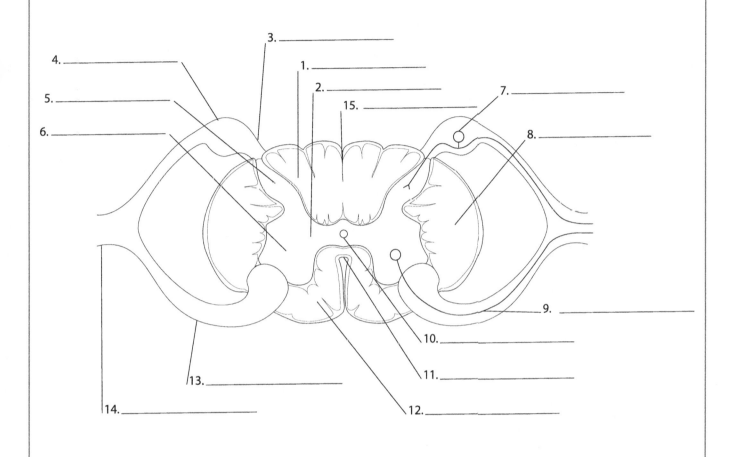

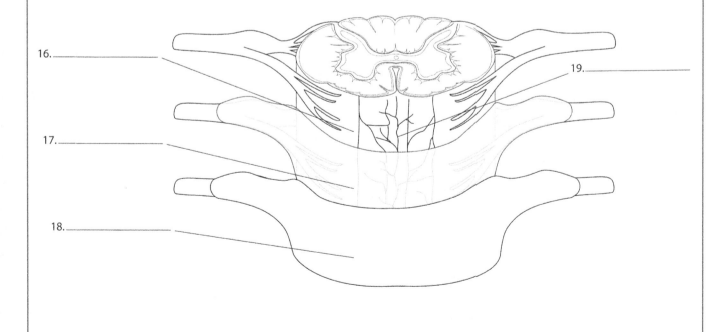

SPINAL CORD ANATOMY

1. White mater
2. Grey mater
3. Dorsal root
4. Dorsal root ganglion
5. Dorsal horn
6. Ventral horn
7. Sensory neuron soma
8. Lateral funiculus
9. Motor neuron
10. Central canal
11. Anterior median fissure
12. Anterior funiculus
13. Ventral root
14. Spinal nerve
15. Posterior median sulcus
16. Pia mater
17. Arachnoid mater
18. Dura mater
19. Vessels

SPINAL CORD TRACTS

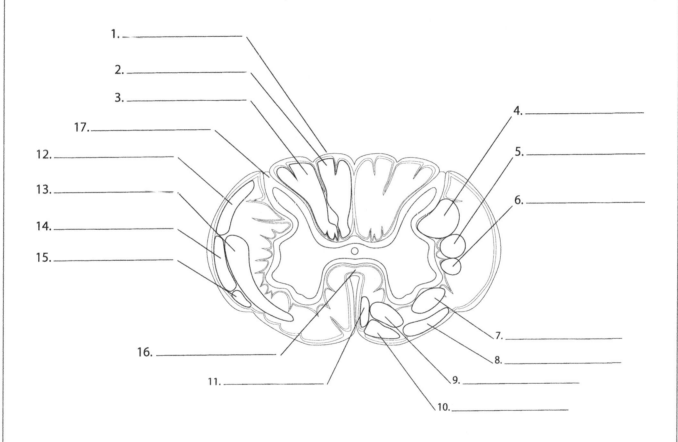

1. _____
2. _____
3. _____
17. _____
12. _____
13. _____
14. _____
15. _____
16. _____
11. _____

4. _____
5. _____
6. _____
7. _____
8. _____
9. _____
10. _____

SPINAL CORD TRACTS

1. Posterior (dorsal) column system

2. Gracile fasciculus

3. Cuneate fasciculus

4. Lateral corticospinal (pyramidal) tract

5. Rubrospinal tract

6. Descending autonomic fibres

7. Medulary (lateral) reticulospinal tract

8. Vestibulospinal tract

9. Pontine (medial) reticulospinal tract

10. Tectospinal tract

11. Anterior (ventral) corticospinal tract

12. Posterior (dorsal) spinocerebellar tract

13. Anterolateral system (5 tracts)

14. Anterior (ventral) spinocerebellar tract

15. Spino-olivary tract

16. Anterior commissure

17. Dorsolateral fasciculus (tract of Lissauer)

Made in the USA
Monee, IL
06 December 2022

20045195R00037